Charles Babbage and his Calculating Engines

Charles Babbage and his Calculating Engines

Doron Swade

SCIENCE MUSEUM

Published by the Science Museum,
Exhibition Road, London SW7 2DD.

Frontispiece

CHARLES BABBAGE IN AN OIL PAINTING
BY SAMUEL LAURENCE

Possibly commissioned by Babbage's
friend and brother-in-law Sir Edward Ryan,
and exhibited at the Royal Academy in
1845. At 53, Babbage is enjoying the
esteem of his contemporaries as scientist,
mechanician and man of letters.

National Portrait Gallery, London

Charles Babbage, 1791-1871

Charles Babbage was born in Walworth, Surrey, on 26 December 1791. He was one of four children born to Benjamin Babbage, a banker, and Elizabeth Plumleigh Teape. His two brothers died in infancy. His sister, Mary Anne, outlived him.

He was schooled near Exeter in Devon, at Enfield, Middlesex, at Cambridge by a clergyman-tutor, at Totnes Grammar School and finally, in classics, by an Oxford tutor. He went to Trinity College, Cambridge, in 1810, graduated from Peterhouse in 1814, and received his MA in 1817.

He took up residence in London in 1815 at 5 Devonshire Street, Portland Place, and moved to 1 Dorset Street, Manchester Square in 1828, where he lived for the rest of his life. He married Georgiana Whitmore in 1814 and had at least eight children, three of whom survived to maturity, Benjamin Herschel, Dugald Bromhead, and Henry Prevost. His wife, his father, and two of his children (Charles and a newborn son) all died in 1827. In 1834, his only daughter, Georgiana, died.

Babbage was elected a fellow of the Royal Society in 1816 and occupied the Lucasian chair of mathematics at Cambridge from 1828 to 1839. Between 1813 and 1868 he published six full length works and nearly ninety papers.

He died on 18 October 1871 and was buried at Kensal Green cemetery in London.

CHARLES BABBAGE AND HIS FIANCÉE GEORGIANA WHITMORE

Portrayed in watercolour miniatures in 1813, when Babbage was a Cambridge undergraduate aged 21. They married in 1814; Babbage was elected FRS two years later. At Cambridge Babbage became close friends with John Herschel, Edward Ryan and George Peacock.

Dr N F Babbage, Australia

Contents

Acknowledgements

Many people helped in the preparation of the Babbage bicentenary exhibition and of this book, and in the building of Difference Engine No. 2. We are grateful to them all, and especially to the following:

Allan G Bromley for proposing to the Science Museum in 1985 that Difference Engine No. 2 be constructed for the Babbage bicentenary. His detailed knowledge of Babbage's engine designs provided the basis for the construction.

Reg Crick and Barrie Holloway, the engineers who translated Babbage's designs into metalwork and built Difference Engine No. 2.

Peter Turvey for curatorial help, particularly his work on the Trial Piece, and Emma Hedderwick for her willing and energetic assistance with tasks too numerous to name. Michael Wright for his advice on nineteenth century workshop practice.

Jim Roberts for his unfailingly generous help with Babbage sources.

Michael Lindgren and Ralf Bülow for their help with the loans from Sweden and Germany respectively.

Dr Stuart Barton Babbage and Dr Neville Francis Babbage for the loan of family memorabilia and other primary source material.

Nordiska Museet, Stockholm, for the loan of the Scheutz prototype difference engine, Tekniska Museet, Stockholm, for the loan of the Wiberg difference engine, and Hessisches Landesmuseum, Darmstadt, for the loan of the Müller calculator.

The staff of the National Portrait Gallery, London, and the Earl of Lytton, Sir Peter Michael, and Mr B E C Howarth-Loomes, for their kind assistance in the loan of portrait material.

List of plates

Foreword

Charles Babbage defies simple typecasting. Scholarly attention has yet to reveal a simple key to the message and meaning of his work. He is most widely known for his work on calculating engines and his reputation as a computer pioneer tends to distort our perception of his place in the larger landscape of nineteenth century thought.

The scope of his interests and activities is impressively wide even by the generous standards of Victorian polymathy. He was an inventor, reformer, mathematician, philosopher, scientist, critic, political economist, and a prolific writer.

Babbage's reputation as a 'computer pioneer' rests largely on his work on the Analytical Engine. The design of this machine, conceived by 1834, has features stunningly similar to those of modern general purpose electronic computers. We are habituated to see precedent as cause, and Babbage is frequently referred to as the 'father', the 'grandfather', or 'forefather' of modern computing. However, the lineage of the modern computer is not as clear cut as these genealogical tributes imply.

There is no unbroken line of development between Babbage's work in the nineteenth century and the modern computer. His Analytical Engine was a developmental cul-de-sac. His efforts represent an isolated episode, a startling and magnificent one, but an episode nonetheless. There is a great gap: the movement that led to the modern computer did not resume until the 1940s when pioneers of the electronic age of computing rediscovered many of the principles explored by Babbage, largely in ignorance of his designs.

However, there is more owing to Babbage than a respectful and perhaps awed salute across a barren gulf of time. His exploits and his aims were an integral part of the folklore shared by the small communities of scientists, mathematicians and engineers who throughout remained involved with tabulation and computation. Babbage's failures were failures of practical accomplishment, not of principle, and the legend of his extraordinary engines was the vehicle not only for the vision but for the unquestioned trust that a universal automatic machine was possible. The electronic age of computing was informed by the spirit and tradition of Babbage's work rather than by any deep knowledge of his designs which have attracted detailed attention only in the last few decades. There *is* therefore a sense in which Babbage can properly be referred to as the 'ancestral figure' in the history of computing. Perhaps not a father or grandfather. More of a great uncle.

Babbage failed to realise a full engine design in physical form and the reasons for this occupy the centre ground in the debate about the significance of his work. The issue is so dominant that the failure to complete any of his engines has become inseparable from the genius of their invention. Factors tossed into the historiographic melting pot include Babbage's personality, the lack of credible progress, personal vendettas, an unresolved dispute with his engineer over compensation, problematic funding, run-away costs, an unfavourable entrepreneurial climate, political change, the cultural divide between pure and applied science, the fact that experts were divided on whether there was any real need, and the shortsightedness of the government for withdrawing support when the project was within sight of completion.

The view most often repeated in histories of computing is that Babbage failed because of limitations of Victorian machine tool technology. Narrowly interpreted this can be taken to imply that parts could not be made with sufficient precision for the machine to work when assembled. This is highly credible, at least at face value. We tend to regard the technological past as crude and to patronise Babbage's cogwheel world from the high ground of modern microelectronics. Curiously, there is no evidence to support this view. Nonetheless the 'limitations of technology' thesis does have something to be said for it, if it is broadened beyond issues of precision to include less readily quantifiable factors – the time and cost implications of manufacturing hundreds of repeat parts in a culture somewhere between the traditions of craft and mass production, the implications of using available technology to its limits, and the social organisation of labour.

The central question that continues to tantalise is whether the circumstances concealed the technical or the logical impossibility of Babbage's dream. The failure to complete Difference Engine No. 1, abandoned in 1833 after a decade of design and engineering effort, was the central trauma in Babbage's scientific life. It is something he returns to repeatedly in his writing as though unable to reconcile himself to the dismal outcome. At different times he expresses outrage, disdain, protest and despair.

In an attempt to resolve or at least illuminate these issues the Science Museum has constructed, for the 1991 bicentenary celebrations, Babbage's Difference Engine No. 2. This is the first full size calculating engine designed by Babbage ever to be completed and was built to the original designs (though without the printer) using parts closely matching those available to Babbage. The engine was designed between 1847 and 1849; with 4,000 parts it measures 7 feet high, 11 feet long, and 18 inches deep (2·1×3·4×0·5 m). It is an object of deep historical interest, a sumptuous piece of engineering sculpture, and a lasting monument to its inventor. Its completion closes an anguished chapter in the prehistory of computing; as an artefact it is already a commemorative icon of Babbage's vision.

The Science Museum has a special relationship with Babbage which predates the construction of the Difference Engine. Its collections contain the seminal objects that are the material legacy of Babbage's endeavours, and its archives hold the most comprehensive set of original manuscripts and design drawings extant. This unique collection of material was supplemented for the exhibition, and for this book, with related primary source material loaned from Australia, Sweden and Germany. Some of this additional material had not been seen in the United Kingdom before. It included family memorabilia, the first complete printing difference engine (the prototype machine finished in 1843 by Georg and Edvard Scheutz in Sweden), the calculator of Johann Müller (1784), and another Swedish difference engine, that of Martin Wiberg (c1860). Collectively the material displayed, and reproduced in this book, represents the most significant collection of Babbage-related artefacts to be gathered in one place in the twentieth century.

The purpose of the book, like that of the exhibition, is to present the material heritage of Babbage's life and work and to trace the course of an heroic but unsuccessful movement to automate calculation in the last century. Its five chapters follow five broad themes which correspond to physical areas in the exhibition: *The Tables Crisis*, *Babbage and Technology*, *'Glory and Failure'* (a title borrowed from a recent study, by Michael Lindgren, of early difference engines), *Computer Pioneer*, and *Polymath*.

The Tables Crisis treats the genesis of Babbage's work on calculating machines – the perceived need to eliminate human errors in mathematical and navigational tables. *Babbage and Technology* is concerned with the design and manufacture of the machines that were invented as a response to the 'crisis'. *'Glory and Failure'* focuses on the honour that history bestows on those who pioneered difference engines, and the heavy personal and financial costs of their efforts. *Computer Pioneer* is concerned primarily with Babbage's work on the Analytical Engine upon which his modern reputation largely rests, while *Polymath* shifts ground to the rich diversity of Babbage's interests outside the field for which he is best known.

The small completed portion of Babbage's Difference Engine No. 1 was exhibited at the International Exhibition of 1862 in London. Babbage was peeved by the small size and obscurity of the display, which he felt was inconsistent with public interest – 'English Engine Poked Into a Hole', he growled. We hope that the Science Museum's bicentenary exhibition – and the book which has sprung from it – would have been spared such censure.

The Tables Crisis

BABBAGE AT 40 YEARS

Shown as Lucasian professor of
mathematics at Cambridge in an
engraving worked by the artist John
Linnell in 1832. *On the economy of machinery
and manufactures* was published in the
same year. The print was published
on 1 January 1833.

Science Museum Library: 1987-1104

*"One is torn between admiration for
his genius and pity for his
wretchedness. But what a man."*
B V Bowden, 1964

Attempts to mechanise calculation in the seventeenth and eighteenth centuries had led to a number of devices to aid arithmetic calculation. Devices by Schickard, Pascal, Leibniz and others were, for all their ingeniousness, in the nature of serious-minded playthings – ornate curiosities of doubtful reliability or robustness, which were by and large unequal to the demands of routine use.

The most persistent difficulty in the design of early mechanical calculators was the problem of 'carry'. Adding 9 to 15, for example, to give 24 requires a 1 to be carried from the units column to the tens column. This is reasonably easy. But when a 1 is added to 999,999, say, to give 1,000,000, each carry triggers a new carry in the next column and seven actions need to be taken as a result of one operation. Difficulties with a 'domino' carry of this kind restricted devices from being extended to more than six or eight figures. It was not until the 1820s that Thomas de Colmar produced a reliable and commercially successful device, his arithmometer, for performing the basic functions of arithmetic.

Until the successful automation of calculation in the twentieth century, scientists, navigators, engineers, surveyors, bankers, actuaries and the like, relied on printed mathematical tables to perform calculations requiring more than a few figures of accuracy.

The production of tables was not only monumentally tedious but prone to error. A contemporary of Babbage, Dionysius Lardner, wrote in 1834 that a random selection of forty volumes of numerical tables contained no fewer than 3,700 acknowledged *errata* and an unknown number of unacknowledged ones.

The cost of unknown errors was difficult to quantify and the stakes, in human and commercial terms, were high. There were rumours of ships going aground because of errors in navigational tables. John Herschel, the astronomer and Babbage's lifelong friend, writing in support of Babbage's work, likened an error in logarithm tables to 'a sunken rock at sea'. In a rare,

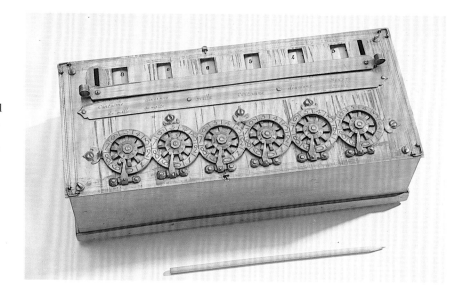

"It is unworthy for excellent men to lose hours like slaves in the labour of calculation which could safely be relegated to anyone else if machines were used."

G W Leibniz, 1685

"An undetected error in a logarithmic table is like a sunken rock at sea yet undiscovered, upon which it is impossible to say what wrecks may have taken place."

Sir John Herschel, 1842

specific example, Babbage cites that the government had lost £2-3 million as a direct result of errors in tables used for annuities.

Tables had three basic sources of error: errors of calculation ('computers' at that time were not machines but fallible human beings who performed routine calculations), errors of transcription introduced when the results were copied into a form suitable to give to a printer, and errors of typesetting and printing.

Babbage was a fastidious analyst of tabular errors. He was a connoisseur of printed tables and his private collection, preserved at the Royal Observatory in Edinburgh, contains some 300 volumes – one of the most comprehensive collections in existence.

The task that seized Babbage in 1821 and was to occupy him on and off for the rest of his life, was to mechanise the production of tables and embody mathematical rule in machine. The 'unerring certainty of mechanism' would free calculation of human error, and having the machine print the results automatically would eliminate the risk of errors in manual transcription and typesetting. The problems of manual computation and table making would be solved at a stroke.

DE COLMAR ARITHMOMETER

The first reliable and commercially successful calculator, introduced c1820. De Colmar-type arithmometers remained in production until about the start of World War I.
Size: 10×59×18 cm.

1967-69

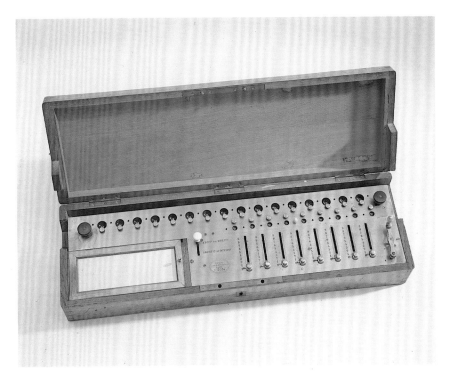

MATHEMATICAL TABLES

Editions of tables were bound in various sizes from large folios to small portable volumes according to use. An edition of *Tabulae* by Regiomontanus, 1584, shown open, has two parts sewn into one bulky volume comprising nearly 400 pages, each 21×16 cm. This selection of tables by renowned mathematicians – Georg von Vega 1794, Adriaan Vlacq 1628, Henry Briggs 1624, François Callet 1795, and French and German editions of Vlacq in 1670 and 1726 – is representative of the range of works that Babbage collected, published over three centuries.

Science Museum Library

TABULAE DER SINUUM BY VLACQ

Publishers of mathematical tables showed keen business acumen in recognising the market for compact editions for portable use. Vlacq's tables were very large. In 1636 he published a small volume of tables carried to seven places, which was a popular success. The tables were often reprinted and reedited, and were translated into French (left) and German (right). The French edition of 1670 carried a decorative engraved title page in Latin, featuring the muses of astronomy, geometry and mathematics – symbolic of the applications for tables – at their calculative art, surrounded by instruments and books. Despite the pocket size of 17×11 cm, the tables took up more than 300 pages.

Science Museum Library

TABVLÆ
SINUUM,
TANGENTIVM,
ET SECANTIVM,
ET
LOGARITHMO-
RVM

LVGDVNI
Apud IOANNEM THIOLY, *vico*
Mercatorio sub signo Palmæ, 1670.

Minut.	86 Grad.				
	Sinus	Tang.	Secans	Log.Sin.	Log.Tan.
60	99862.95	1908113.7	1910732.3	9.9994044	11.2806042
59	99861.42	1897552.3	1900185.4	9.9993978	11.2781937
58	99859.89	1887106.8	1889754.5	9.9993811	11.2757965
57	99858.35	1876775.4	1879437.6	9.9993844	11.2734122
56	99856.80	1866556.2	1869233.0	9.9993776	11.2710411
55	99855.24	1856447.3	1859138.7	9.9993708	11.2686826
54	99853.67	1846447.1	1849153.0	9.9993640	11.2663369
53	99852.09	1836553.7	1839274.2	9.9993572	11.2640036
52	99850.50	1826765.4	1829500.5	9.9993503	11.2616826
51	99848.91	1817080.7	1819830.3	9.9993433	11.2593742
50	99847.31	1807497.7	1810261.9	9.9993364	11.2570778
49	99845.70	1798015.0	1800793.7	9.9993293	11.2547933
48	99844.08	1788631.0	1791424.3	9.9993223	11.2525208
47	99842.45	1779344.2	1782152.0	9.9993151	11.2502600
46	99840.81	1770153.9	1772975.3	9.9993081	11.2480108
45	99839.16	1761055.9	1763892.8	9.9993009	11.2457732
44	99837.51	1752051.6	1754903.0	9.9992938	11.2435469
43	99835.85	1743138.7	1746004.6	9.9992865	11.2413319
42	99834.18	1734315.5	1737196.0	9.9992793	11.2391281
41	99832.50	1725580.9	1728476.1	9.9992498	11.2304223
40	99830.81	1716933.7	1719843.4	9.9992646	11.2347535
39	99829.11	1708372.4	1711296.6	9.9992572	11.2325825
38	99827.41	1699895.7	1702834.6	9.9992498	11.2304223
37	99825.70	1691502.5	1694455.9	9.9992424	11.2282726
36	99823.98	1683191.5	1686159.4	9.9992349	11.2261335
35	99822.25	1674961.4	1677943.9	9.9992274	11.2240048
34	99820.51	1666811.2	1669808.2	9.9992198	11.2218864
33	99818.76	1658739.6	1661751.2	9.9992122	11.2197782
32	99817.01	1650745.5	1653771.7	9.9992046	11.2176801
31	99815.25	1642827.9	1645868.6	9.9991969	11.2155921
30	99813.48	1634985.6	1638040.8	9.9991892	11.2135139

"My friend Herschel, calling upon me, brought with him the calculations of the computers, and we commenced the tedious process of verification. After a time many discrepancies occurred, and at one point these discordances were so numerous that I exclaimed 'I wish to God these calculations had been executed by steam'."

Charles Babbage, recalling the genesis of his work on calculating machines. The meeting with Herschel took place in 1821.

Babbage conceived of his Difference Engine to do just this. Unlike the calculators of Schickard, Pascal and Leibniz, the difference engine was not designed to perform ordinary day-to-day arithmetic but to calculate a series of numerical values and automatically print the results. Difference engines are so called because of the principle upon which they are based – the method of finite differences. This principle was well-known at the time and was used by human computers in the preparation of tables.

Finding the value of many mathematical functions requires multiplications, divisions, additions and subtractions. The advantage of the method of differences is that it eliminates the need for multiplication and division by reducing the process to a succession of simple additions. And addition is far easier to mechanise than multiplication or division.

The idea of a machine to perform calculation and tabulation *automatically* was a milestone in the history of computing.

ARITHMETICA LOGARITHMICA BY VLACQ, 1628

Adriaan Vlacq republished these logarithm tables in 1628 in an edition of 1000 copies with Latin, Dutch and French prefaces. This was an immediate sell-out. At quarto size (33×22 cm) and 855 pages thick, Vlacq's work had comparatively few errors and formed the basis for tables for many years.

Science Museum Library

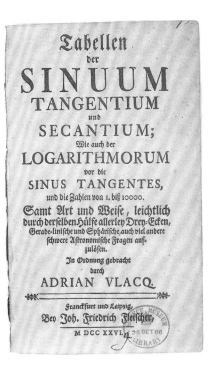

THESAURUS LOGARITHMORUM COMPLETUS BY GEORG VON VEGA, 1794

The task of calculating, printing and checking tables was a massive and formidable one. Tables were computed from scratch only when necessary. Whenever possible, tables were derived from existing sources, which were corrected, revised and expanded. Babbage published a set of logarithm tables in 1827, which had a reputation for accuracy. Their preparation involved nine separate stages of checking and proofreading. Vega's logarithm tables, which were among the most reliable available to Babbage, were used as a source. Size: folio.

Science Museum Library

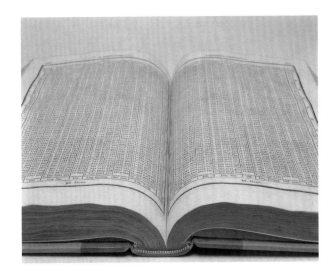

Babbage and Technology

ENGRAVING OF BABBAGE BY R C ROFFE

Issued as a frontispiece to *Mechanics Magazine*, vol. XVIII, October 1832 – March 1833. In the latter part of 1832 problems had ensued between Babbage, now 41, and his engineer Joseph Clement. Work on the first Difference Engine stopped entirely in 1833.

Science Museum Library: 1983-1423

Babbage designed two kinds of engines, Difference Engines and Analytical Engines. By previous standards these engines were monumental in conception, physical size and complexity.

Manufacturing parts for his engines stretched the standards of engineering practice. Their intricate shapes required special jigs and tools, and the need for hundreds of near-identical precision parts challenged an engineering culture somewhere between craft and mass production traditions.

Babbage built a small experimental model of a Difference Engine in 1822. He suspected that the 'art of construction' in the 1820s was not sufficiently advanced to meet the demands of a larger machine. In 1823 he conducted a survey of manufacturing techniques visiting industrial centres in England and Scotland. He constantly monitored progress in the industrial arts, visiting workshops and factories whenever he could both at home and on the Continent. His major influential work on political economy, *On the economy of machinery and manufactures* (1832) was a result of these researches.

Babbage was himself an amateur machinist and introduced several improvements to tools, machinery and workshop technique, often in collaboration with his engineer, Joseph Clement. It was argued by some that the spin-off benefit to the machine tool industry justified the large investment of public money in the Difference Engine project despite its overall failure.

The complexity of the engines made demands on the design process as well as manufacture. Babbage explored his designs in 'scribbling books' which survive as a vast unpublished manuscript archive in the Science Museum Library in London. He made cardboard cutouts of parts to visualise and verify their operation and he experimented incessantly with small trial mechanisms to test and simplify his ideas. His draughtsmen produced meticulous design drawings many of which are the finest examples of the draughtsman's art to that time.

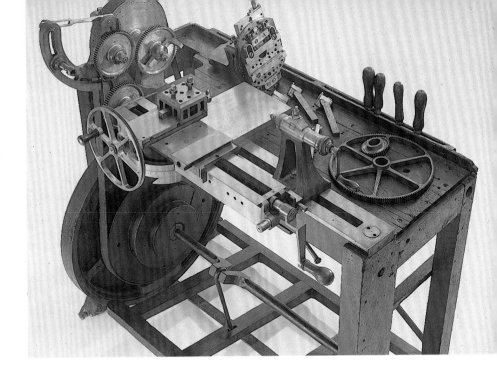

BABBAGE'S LATHE

Multi-purpose lathe owned by Charles Babbage. His son, H P Babbage, records that it was made to order by Joseph Clement in 1823-24.

1878-89

CAM-PLATE AND DIE, c1870

Babbage's use of pressure die-casting for the quantity production of interchangeable parts is among the earliest documented uses of this technique. The sample casting shown is a cam-plate with gear segment for the carriage mechanism of the Analytical Engine. Components from such moulds date from at least as early as 1869.

1905-181pt

Babbage was particularly proud of his Mechanical Notation – a method of describing the complex motions of large numbers of interconnected parts. The Notation was a symbolic shorthand to describe combinations of parts too complicated to visualise all at once. It was used both to describe and to optimise his designs.

For Babbage the Notation was not confined to mechanical devices but was a general descriptive language, albeit an abstract one. He gives, as examples of its use, 'combat by sea or land' and 'the functions of animal life'. He himself used the Notation a great deal and constantly refined it. But for all his pride in its invention, it was largely ignored.

CARDBOARD CUTOUTS FOR DIFFERENCE ENGINE NO. 1, 1831

Babbage used cardboard cutouts of various components while developing his designs. The selection shown includes two examples of 'wings' fixed to conventional gearwheels. The 'wings' are variable diameter gears which mesh with starting pinions. The purpose of the arrangement was to reduce starting torque and initial acceleration. Over 132 separate cutouts of various parts survive. Many of the annotations are in Babbage's hand and give clues about the contribution made by his engineer, Joseph Clement, to the design process.

1971-266pt

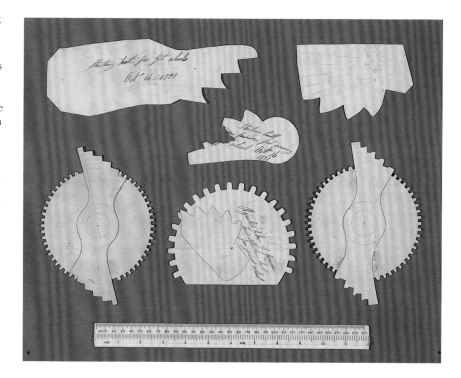

DRAWINGS CABINET

One of three wooden cabinets made to store Babbage's design drawings. The drawings hang vertically from tabs. The lid houses two extension arms. With the cabinet open the arms can be fitted to hang a drawing for display. Presented by H P Babbage in 1878. Size: 87×112×44 cm.

Science Museum Library: 1878-5pt

EXPERIMENTAL ASSEMBLY

Babbage experimented incessantly with trial models. This is a small experimental assembly, one of a few that survive.

1905-181pt

The development of Difference Engine No. 1, the largest of Babbage's practical ventures, was under way in 1824. This vast machine called for an estimated 25,000 parts, would have weighed several tons, and measured 8 feet high, 7 feet long and 3 feet deep ($2\cdot4\times2\cdot1\times0\cdot9$ m). Babbage hired Joseph Clement, a skilled toolmaker and draughtsman – a prized and none too common combination at the time – to build the machine. The years of design, development and manufacture that followed were the most gruelling and ultimately disappointing of Babbage's life. Work stopped in 1833 after a dispute with Clement over compensation for moving his workshops to premises alongside Babbage's house.

SCRIBBLING BOOK, 1836

Babbage kept informal work books known as 'scribbling books' or 'sketchbooks'. These document his designs, exploratory schemes and other deliberations. The volumes collectively contain between 6,000 and 7,000 pages of manuscript.

Science Museum Library: BAB [S] 15

CHARLES BABBAGE'S DIFFERENCE ENGINE NO. 1 – PORTION, 1832

This portion of the engine, assembled by Joseph Clement in 1832, is the first known automatic calculator. It represents about one seventh of the calculating mechanism of the full size engine which was not completed. The portion shown has nearly 2,000 individual parts, and is one of the finest examples of precision engineering of the time. Size: 72×59×61 cm.

1862-89

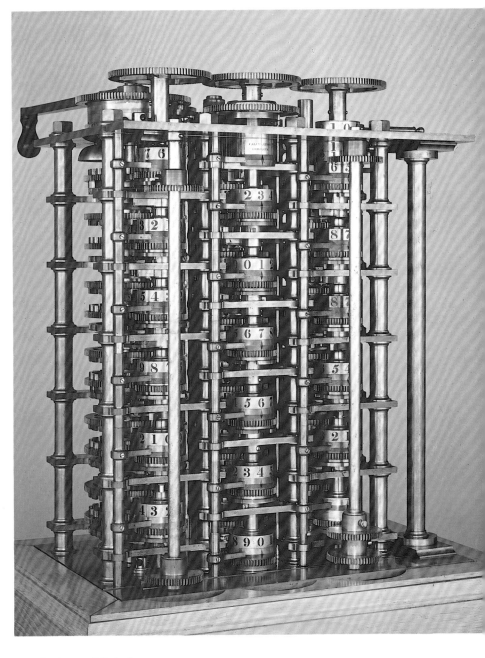

THE FIRST SCHEUTZ DIFFERENCE ENGINE

The first printing calculator by Georg and Edvard Scheutz, Sweden. This prototype produced the first tables calculated and printed by machinery. Its construction is much cruder than that of Babbage's Difference Engine. This raises questions about whether the precision sought by Babbage was always necessary. Size: 54×86×65 cm.

Nordiska Museet, Stockholm

Accounts vary on how close to completion the engine was when work stopped. What seems clear is that a substantial number of essential parts for the calculating mechanism had been made and assembly was a realistic prospect. On Babbage's instruction Clement assembled a small section of the engine as a demonstration piece. This 'finished portion of the unfinished engine', completed in 1832, represents about one seventh of the calculating part of the full machine. The printing mechanism was not assembled.

The portion of the Difference Engine completed in 1832 still works and is one of the finest examples of precision engineering of the time. It was of practical use to Babbage in tabulating certain functions and also became a conversation piece at his Saturday evening soirées where he used it to elaborate on his theory of miracles. Its successful completion has been used as a formidable argument in support of Babbage's conviction that the full sized machine was a practical prospect.

This portion of Difference Engine No. 1 is the first known automatic calculating device and is one of the most celebrated icons in the prehistory of computing.

By the end of 1834 Babbage had conceived of a more ambitious and technically more demanding machine. This was the Analytical Engine – a revolutionary machine upon which much of Babbage's fame as a computer pioneer rests. This engine called for more near-identical parts than even the Difference Engine. Daunted perhaps by the fate of the Difference Engine, Babbage expected that if he built an Analytical Engine it would be at his own expense. He looked for an alternative to machining hundreds of repeat parts and investigated pressure die-casting and stamping sheet metal as a way of reducing costs. A simplified portion of the engine was all that was built in his lifetime. This, and a piece built by his son after Babbage's death, a few small experimental assemblies, and the designs, are the physical legacy of a remarkable intellectual achievement of the nineteenth century.

13   *Babbage and Technology*

"It is not a bad definition of man to describe him as a tool-making animal."
Charles Babbage, 1851

"The whole history of this invention has been a struggle against time."
Charles Babbage, 1837

The distinction of completing the first working difference engine goes to a Swedish father and son team, Georg and Edvard Scheutz. Inspired by accounts of the Babbage engine, they completed, in 1843, a prototype engine based on an account of Babbage's scheme but largely of their own design. This machine produced the first tables calculated and printed by machinery.

In the Scheutzes' machine the problem of replicating results without risk of human error was solved in the way Babbage had intended – by impressing the numbers on *papier mâché* (flong) or soft metal strips. These were used as moulds for stereotype plates from which multiple copies of the results could be printed.

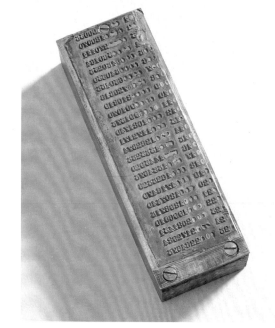

SCHEUTZ STEREOTYPE PLATE, c1849

A stereotype plate from the difference engine completed in 1843 by Edvard Scheutz. It was used to print the first tables calculated and stereotyped by machinery. Leading zeroes were removed before printing.
Size: 2.5×4.5×12.5 cm.

Nordiska Museet, Stockholm

DESIGN DRAWING: DIFFERENCE ENGINE
NO. 1, 1830

Plan and side elevation of Babbage's
Difference Engine No. 1. The physical
engine would have measured 8 feet high,
7 feet wide and 3 feet deep
(2.4×0.9×2.1 m). The drawing shows a
version that calculates with sixteen digits
and seven orders of difference.
Size: 60×94 cm.

Science Museum Library: BAB [U1] a

The first Scheutz engine was built using simple hand tools and a primitive lathe. In comparison with the sophistication of Babbage's and Clement's equipment, the means available to Edvard Scheutz were decidedly crude. The successful demonstration of the Scheutz engine with its comparatively rough construction raises questions as to whether the high degree of precision to which Clement worked was in all instances necessary.

The engine was rediscovered in 1979 by a young Swedish historian, Michael Lindgren, who traced the forgotten machine to the Nordiska Museet, Stockholm, where it had been deposited in 1881.

MECHANICAL NOTATION, 1847

An example of Babbage's use of his Notation, taken from a design drawing for Difference Engine No. 2. The system of letters and indices identifies parts and describes their motion and relation to other parts in the mechanism.

Science Museum Library: BAB [A] 171

ANALYTICAL ENGINE – DETAIL, c1871

A view of the experimental model of the
Analytical Engine under construction at
the time of Babbage's death in 1871.
Shows the high degree of repetition in the
calculating mechanism and the need for
large numbers of near-identical parts.
An example of Babbage's use of pressure
die-casting.

1878-3

'Glory and Failure'

"Mr Babbage's projects appear to be so indefinitely expensive, the ultimate success so problematical, and the expenditure certainly so large and so utterly incapable of being calculated, that the Government would not be justified in taking upon itself any further liability."

Lord Derby for Benjamin Disraeli, Chancellor of the Exchequer, 1852

Charles Babbage failed to realise any complete engine in physical form. The reasons for this remain the subject of analysis and energetic debate.

After Clement's last payment in 1834 the cost to the government of the Difference Engine project was £17,470. This was a massive sum: the steam locomotive, *John Bull*, completed by Robert Stephenson and Co. for shipment to America in 1831, cost £784 7s. The failure to complete an engine was the central trauma in Babbage's scientific life and something he brooded over repeatedly.

The Scheutzes completed three difference engines – a prototype and two 'production' machines. The second two machines were sold, one to the Dudley Observatory in Albany, New York State, and the other to the General Register Office in London. The Albany machine was little used. The Register Office machine was used to produce the *English life table* published in 1864. Both these machines were more troublesome to use than expected.

THE THIRD SCHEUTZ DIFFERENCE ENGINE, 1859

This engine is a copy (with minor modifications) of the Scheutzes' second engine completed in 1853. It was built by Bryan Donkin in London for the General Register Office (GRO) where it was used to prepare the English life table published in 1864. Donkin reported that the machine consisted of about 4,320 parts. It was sold to the GRO for £1,200 and was £615 over budget on completion. The machine calculated with four orders of difference to fifteen figures and stereotyped results to eight figures. Size: 45×187×52 cm.

1914-122/1

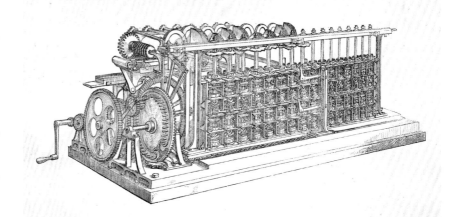

THE SECOND SCHEUTZ ENGINE

Frontispiece of specimen tables produced using the second Scheutz engine. The fifty page booklet was sent to about 400 potential customers and benefactors. It is dedicated to Babbage 'by his sincere admirers, Georg and Edvard Scheutz'. The image of the engine is from an engraving that appeared in the *Illustrated London News,* 30 June 1855. To indicate the modest power requirements, the article in the *ILN* suggests that the engine could be driven by a small dog in a treadmill cage. *Specimens* was the first collection of tables produced by machine.

1914-122/3

The Scheutz engines worked after a fashion but were not commercially successful. Georg Scheutz was honoured by his country for his achievements. He died in 1873 practically bankrupt. Five years later his son, Edvard, died bankrupt and in debt.

There were other attempts to build difference engines in the nineteenth century – Alfred Deacon in London, Martin Wiberg in Sweden and Barnard Grant in America. Deacon's machine was never completed. The Wiberg machine, completed in about 1860, was used to produce a large volume of tables published in Swedish, German, French and English. The history of the Wiberg calculator was financially fraught. Grant's engine was exhibited at the Centennial Exhibition in Philadelphia in 1876. It attracted attention which was shortlived.

The nineteenth century movement to mechanise and automate mechanical calculation had failed. The pioneers of the movement, Babbage and the Scheutzes, are honoured with the distinction of their pioneering efforts. All suffered personally and financially as a result.

ENGLISH LIFE TABLE, 1864

The third Scheutz engine was used in the production of life assurance tables. The volume contains 590 pages of printed tables. The numbers in larger type have been stereotyped by the engine. The smaller type appears to have been set by hand.

1914-122/4

CALCULATOR OF JOHANN MÜLLER, 1784

Johann Müller's 'universal' calculator. The mechanism is based on Leibniz's stepped drum. It was designed for standard arithmetical operations and could calculate to fourteen figures. It had a warning bell to alert the user to incorrect settings. Müller is thought to have been the first to suggest a printing calculator and the first to propose that the method of differences could be used to calculate arithmetical series.
Size: 13 cm (high) ×30.cm (diameter).

Hessisches Landesmuseum, Darmstadt

STEREOTYPE PLATES AND MOULDS

The Scheutz engines impressed results on strips of *papier mâché* or soft metal. These were removed from the machine and used as moulds to make stereotype plates for use in a printing press.
Rear: stack of *papier mâché* strips.
Front: printing plates.

1914-122/5pt

Difference Engine No. 2 was built at the
Science Museum to original designs, for
the bicentenary of Babbage's birth. It is
the first of Babbage's calculating engines
to be completed. It consists of 4,000 parts
(excluding the printing mechanism),
weighs over three tons, and is made of
bronze, steel and cast iron. It has seven
orders of difference and is designed to
calculate to thirty figures. The highest
order difference is on the right. The least
significant digit is at the bottom of each
of the figure wheel stacks. The machine
is operated by turning a handle. The
printing mechanism was not built.
Size: 2.1×3.4×0.5 m.

Babbage was not the first to suggest a printing calculator nor was he the
first to consider the method of differences as a suitable principle upon which
to base a calculating machine. This distinction belongs to Johann Müller
(1746-1830) an engineer and master builder.

In a letter written in 1784 Müller refers to a machine he considered building
which would calculate and print any arithmetic progression – 'all one has to
do is to turn a handle'. This letter contains the earliest known description of
a printing calculator. In another letter written in the same year he describes
plans for a machine for calculating squares and cubes by a series of
differences. Müller had conceived of a difference engine 36 years before
Babbage. Details were published in 1786 in a book, key sections of which
were translated for Babbage by John Herschel. The date of this translation
is uncertain and the question of whether some of Babbage's ideas on
difference engines came from Müller remains open.

The completed calculating part of
Babbage's Difference Engine No. 2, with
the two engineers who built it, Reg Crick
(right) and Barrie Holloway (left).

23   *'Glory and Failure'*

DAGUERREOTYPE BY ANTOINE
CLAUDET, 1847-51

Babbage, now in his late fifties, began
work in 1847 on the design of his second
Difference Engine. In the King William
Street studio he and Claudet experimented
during this time with photography of
specimens of colours on porcelain, and
Babbage sat for several portraits.

National Portrait Gallery, London

The reasons for Babbage's failure continue to exercise historians. Factors cited include Babbage's allegedly difficult personality, unconvincing progress, personal enmities, a dispute with Joseph Clement, problematic funding, unsympathetic entrepreneurial climate, several changes of government, cultural conflict between pure and applied science, the fact that experts were divided on whether there was any real need, and lack of government vision when withdrawing support.

The view most often repeated in histories of computing is that Babbage failed because of limitations in Victorian machine tool technology.

To investigate this the Science Museum has constructed Babbage's Difference Engine No. 2. Babbage designed this machine between 1847 and 1849. It is a simpler and more elegant version of the earlier design and benefits from work he had done on the Analytical Engine – a much more complex and therefore more demanding machine to design. He offered the designs for his new engine to the Government in 1852 but no attempt was made to build it.

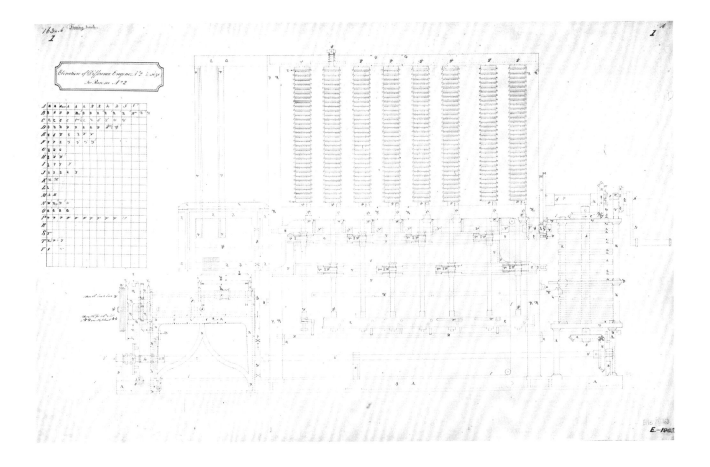

DESIGN DRAWING: DIFFERENCE ENGINE
NO. 2, 1847

Elevation of Difference Engine No. 2,
one of twenty main drawings and several
tracings of the engine. The machine is
operated by turning the handle on the
right. This operates the vertical stack of
fourteen pairs of cams which determine
the action and timing of the calculating
cycle. The calculating part is located on
the top of the machine and consists of

eight columns of thirty one figure wheels.
Below the calculating part are a series of
levers and racks which are activated by
links from the cams to lift, lower and turn
the vertical axes to perform the addition
of differences. The results are printed or
stereotyped by the mechanism on the
left. The printing and stereotyping
mechanism is directly coupled to the last
column of figure wheels. Size: 61×96 cm.

Science Museum Library: BAB [A] 163

WIBERG'S DIFFERENCE ENGINE, c1860

Wiberg's calculator had the same capacity as the later Scheutz machines (four orders of difference and fifteen digits) but was about a tenth of the size. It used identical metal discs arranged linearly along an axis instead of columns or rows of figure wheels as in the Babbage and Scheutz engines. Results were stereotyped on *papier mâché* or soft metal strips.

Size: 23×42×21.5 cm.

Tekniska Museet, Stockholm

Difference Engine No. 2 has 4,000 parts (excluding the printing mechanism). It weighs an estimated three tons and measures 7 feet high, 11 feet long, and 18 inches deep (2·1×3·4×0·5 m). It is built to original designs out of materials closely matching those available to Babbage. The printing mechanism has not been built. Until the start of the project no attempt had been made to construct this machine.

The original set of 20 drawings fully describe the engine but do not specify dimensions, tolerances, finish, choice of materials or methods of manufacture. This information was supplied from knowledge of nineteenth century practice, measurements taken from Babbage's completed assemblies, and analysis of the composition of the metal used by Babbage in his earlier machine.

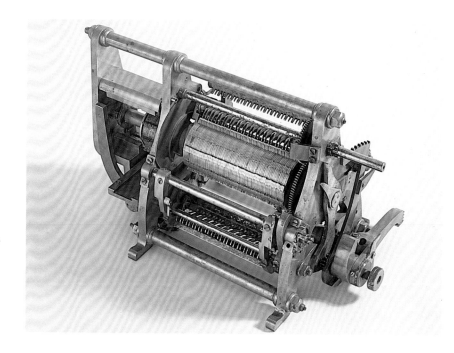

DESIGN DRAWING: DIFFERENCE ENGINE
NO. 2 – DETAIL, 1847

Plan view of a section through the
addition and carriage mechanism. The
two full gear wheels are figure wheels
coupled by an intermediate sector wheel.
The upper part of the drawing shows the
carriage mechanism. The 'fairground
whirl' is a helical arrangement of carry
levers that sample each decade in turn as
part of the 'successive carry' operation.

Science Museum Library: BAB [A] 171

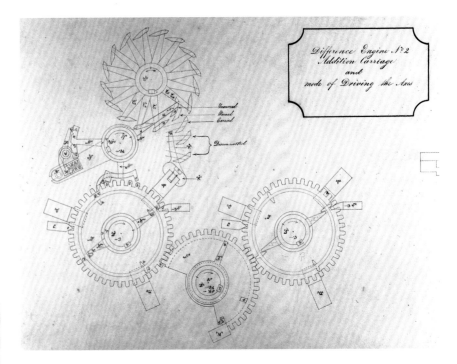

TABLES PRODUCED WITH WIBERG'S
DIFFERENCE ENGINE, 1876

Wiberg's logarithm tables were
published in English in 1876. He observes
in the Preface that aligning the results
was difficult. He also concedes that
'greater typographical beauty' can be
achieved using conventional typesetting
with loose type, but that the 'greater
trustworthiness' of machine-produced
results was worthwhile compensation.

Science Museum Library

TRIAL PIECE FOR BABBAGE'S DIFFERENCE ENGINE NO. 2, 1989

Portion of the calculating mechanism of Difference Engine No. 2. Made by the Science Museum to verify the design of the basic adding element for the full scale engine. The device adds two two-digit numbers and takes account of carry. It is manually operated by lifting and turning the axes from above in a fixed sequence. The full scale machine performs the calculating cycle automatically. Size: 34.5×43×30 cm.

FIGURE WHEEL FOR BABBAGE'S DIFFERENCE ENGINE NO. 2, 1990

One of 248 figure wheels. Each has four decades of numerals. The outer four nibs set a warning mechanism in the event of a carry. The wheels were machined from individual cast billets of bronze. The nibs were press-fitted cold.

Modern techniques were used in the manufacture of repeat parts, but care was taken to make no part with more precision than is known to have been achievable by Babbage.

Difference Engine No. 2 was the first full sized Babbage calculating engine to be completed and was made for display at the 1991 exhibition commemorating the bicentennial year of Babbage's birth. The engine is a research object, an engineering sculpture, and a monument to its inventor.

CHARLES BABBAGE'S DIFFERENCE
ENGINE NO. 2 – DETAIL, 1991

View of the rear of the engine showing the carriage mechanism, which is repeated 210 times. Repeat parts were made by modern manufacturing techniques and are interchangeable.

CARRY LEVER FOR BABBAGE'S
DIFFERENCE ENGINE NO. 2, 1990

One of 210 levers for the carriage mechanism, with a modern fully dimensioned piece-part drawing for the component.

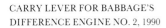

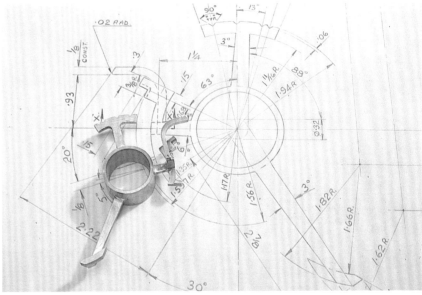

Computer Pioneer

DRAWING BY SAMUEL LAURENCE, c1835-37

Possibly for an oil exhibited in 1837 at the Royal Academy. At 45 years the mechanician seems visibly hounded by continuing disputes with Clement and the government. He had already turned his attention to the Analytical Engine, and to founding the Statistical Society in 1834. His philosophical work *The Ninth Bridgewater treatise* was published in 1837.

Sir Peter Michael

Charles Babbage is most widely known as a computer pioneer. In the light of developments in the twentieth century, his work on the Analytical Engine seems startlingly prescient. It is on this that his reputation as a computer pioneer largely rests.

The desktop mechanical calculators available in Babbage's day relied for their operation on the continuous informed intervention of the user. The Difference Engine, on the other hand, was *automatic*: it did not require specialised knowledge of mathematics or of the internal principles of operation. Mathematical rule was embodied in mechanism and the user supplied physical rather than mental effort in producing useful results.

The Difference Engine was not a *general purpose* machine. It could process numbers entered into it only by adding them in a particular sequence. The Analytical Engine, on the other hand, was automatic and general purpose. The mathematical tasks that it performed were determined by the user.

Babbage had conceived of the Analytical Engine by 1834, shortly after the Difference Engine project had collapsed. The engine was conceived as a universal machine for finding the value of almost any algebraic function. The Analytical Engine is not a single physical machine but a succession of designs that Babbage refined at intervals until his death in 1871.

The concept of the engine and the detail of its design embody many features of modern electronic computers. The engine was programmable using punched cards – a technique used in the Jacquard Loom to control the patterns woven with thread. It had a 'store' where numbers and intermediate results were held, and a separate 'mill' where the arithmetic processing was performed. The separation of the 'store' and 'mill' is a fundamental feature of the internal organisation of modern computers.

In operation the engine was capable of conditional branching – choosing one of a number of alternative actions depending on a predetermined condition being met (a form of IF... THEN ...). It was also capable of 'looping' – repeating the same sequence of instructions a specifiable number of times.

DESIGN DRAWING: PLAN OF THE ANALYTICAL ENGINE, 1840

Plan of the Analytical Engine showing the general arrangement of the machine. A circle usually represents a column of gears or wheels viewed from above. The store (memory) is to the right and shows sixteen registers. Babbage considered machines with 100 to 1000 such registers. The mill (arithmetic unit) is distributed around the large central circle. The design catered for numbers with forty digits. Size: 61×92 cm.

Science Museum Library: BAB [A] 89*

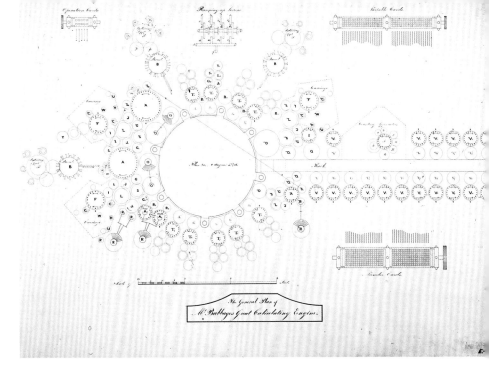

PUNCHED CARDS FOR THE ANALYTICAL ENGINE

Instructions and data were entered into the Analytical Engine using punched cards. In Babbage's design for the card reader the perforated cards were pressed onto a set of rods. Where there were holes, the rods poked through the card and were left unmoved; rods opposite hole-positions that were covered, were activated. The smaller cards are Operation Cards. These specified the arithmetic operations to be performed. The larger cards are Variable Cards. These dictate the 'addresses' of the columns in store where the numbers to be operated on are to be found and where results should be placed. Size: 13×5.5 cm, 18.5×7.0 cm.

1905-181pt

Another technically 'modern' feature was micro-programming – a form of control in which a group of more elementary instructions are performed to produce a single complex action. Babbage also considered parallel processing – performing more than one calculation at the same time.

The physical engine would have been the size of a small locomotive – 15 feet high, 6 feet across in places and, in one version, 20 feet long (4·6×6·1×1·8 m). There would have been little prospect of operating a machine of this size by hand. Had it been built, 'calculating by steam' would have been a prophetic wish come true.

Both the Difference and Analytical Engines are decimal digital machines. The value of a number is represented by the positions of toothed wheels with decimal numerals marked in them. Each digit position in the number has its own wheel and only discrete positions of the wheels are valid representations of numbers. The number 1·5, for example, would be represented by the 'ones' wheel set at '1' and an adjacent separate wheel, the 'tenths' wheel set to '5'. The 'ones' wheel set half way between '1' and '2' would be mechanically disallowed.

Babbage made little concerted attempt to raise funds to build an Analytical Engine. He wrote wishfully of two schemes for raising money for the venture – writing a novel and building a games automaton to play noughts and crosses with a view to charging the public for competing against it. He continued to work on simpler and cheaper methods of manufacturing parts, and built a small trial model which was under construction at the time of his death. This experimental piece, alongside the completed portion of Difference Engine No. 1, is the second great icon in the prehistory of computing.

Babbage published little in the way of technical detail of the Analytical Engine though a large archive of his work survives in the form of unpublished manuscripts and drawings. A paper describing the principles of the engine appeared in 1842 written by an Italian engineer, Luigi

PORTRAIT OF J M JACQUARD WOVEN IN SILK, c1839

This portrait was woven using a Jacquard loom controlled by punched cards. The cards, strung together in a sequence, determined the pattern of the weave. A small model of a Jacquard loom appears on the left behind the seated figure. The punched card system for Babbage's Analytical Engine derives from a loom of this kind. Babbage showed a copy of the portrait hanging in his living room to Prince Albert in 1842. The portrait was made by the firm of Didier Petit et Cie, Lyon; the original oil portrait was by Claude Bonnefond. Size: 51×36 cm.

1942-59

ANALYTICAL ENGINE, 1871

Portion of the mill of the Analytical Engine with printing mechanism, under construction at the time of Babbage's death. The horizontal racks transfer numbers between the two columns of number wheels in the centre and to the printing mechanism on the right.

1878-3

"The marvellous pulp and fibre of a brain had been substituted by brass and iron, he had taught wheelwork to think."

H W Buxton, 1870s

DIFFERENCE ENGINE NO. 1, DEMONSTRATION MODEL – DETAIL

Babbage's Difference and Analytical Engines are decimal digital machines: they use the decimal number system and only discrete positions of the figure wheels are valid representations of a number. In Difference Engine No. 1 the action of the roller on the semi-circular segments is designed to 'digitise' the movement of the wheel. In Difference Engine No. 2 Babbage uses a different technique, driving a wedge between the teeth to correct any derangement and to jam the machine in the event of indeterminate wheel positions.

1967-70

"The labours of Mr Babbage . . . are a marvel of mechanical ingenuity and resource."

C W Merrifield, 1878

"If Babbage had lived 75 years later, I would have been out of a job."

Howard Aiken, pioneer of electronic computing, 1940s

DIFFERENCE ENGINE NO. 1, DEMONSTRATION MODEL

One of about six demonstration pieces put together by Henry Babbage after his father's death in 1871. It was assembled from unused parts left over from the original Difference Engine project. This model was sent to University College, London. Others were sent to Harvard, USA and Cambridge University. A model similar to this, offered to Harvard in 1896, came to the attention of Howard Aiken, an early pioneer of modern computing. It represents one of the tenuous links between Babbage's work and the electronic era.
Size: 30×38×33 cm.

1967-70

Menabrea, following Babbage's visit to Turin in 1840 where he lectured on his work. This 'sketch' was translated from the French by Ada Lovelace, daughter of Lord Byron. Lovelace added lengthy notes to the original article in close consultation with Babbage, whom she greatly admired.

Lovelace's paper contained a detailed and penetrating explanation of the significance of the Analytical Engine, and of its implications for computational method. Her achievement is additionally exceptional given that intellectual pursuits by women were inhibited by the culture of the times. Babbage was aware of the value of her work in explaining his invention. He referred to her as 'the Enchantress of Numbers' and addressed her in a letter as 'my dear and much admired Interpreter'.

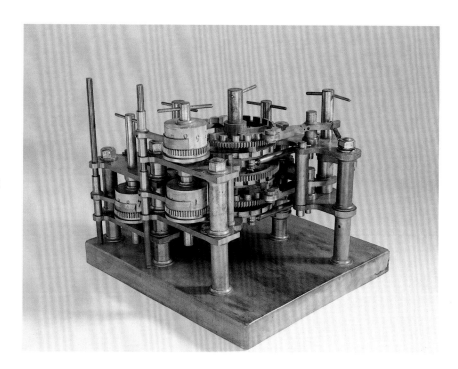

PORTRAIT OF ADA LOVELACE. c1844

'Enchantress of numbers': tinted photograph, from a daguerreotype. It shows Ada at about the time of publication of her translation of Menabrea's memoir on the Analytical Engine. She died in 1852 aged 36.

The Earl of Lytton

"The Analytical Engine weaves algebraic patterns just as the Jacquard loom weaves flowers and leaves."
Ada Lovelace, 1834

ROYAL MAIL SPECIAL ISSUE STAMP, 1991

Babbage repeatedly expressed a sense of injustice at the lack of recognition for his work. He maintained that the Lucasian chair of mathematics at Cambridge was the only honour he received in his own country. A set of stamps issued on 5 March 1991 commemorated British scientific achievements. Four British scientist/engineers were honoured in the set, Charles Babbage (computers), Michael Faraday (electricity), Robert Watson-Watt (radar) and Frank Whittle (jet engine).

Royal Mail Stamp

The line of influence between Babbage's work and modern electronic computers is at best tenuous. Pioneers of electronic computing in the 1940s were informed by the spirit and tradition of Babbage's work rather than by any deep knowledge of his designs which have attracted detailed attention only in the last few decades.

Babbage's youngest son, Henry Prevost, had shown a strong interest in his father's work. After his father's death he built a hand-operated printing calculator based on plans for the mill of the Analytical Engine. This was a four-function calculator designed for addition, subtraction, multiplication and division. He worked on this device intermittently until 1910.

Henry Babbage also assembled about six small demonstration models of the calculating mechanism of Difference Engine No. 1 after his father's death. He offered models to various universities including Harvard in the USA.

The Harvard model came to the attention of Howard Aiken, probably in the late 1930s. Aiken, an early pioneer of modern computing, recalls that it was these 'calculating wheels' that led him to Babbage's work. Aiken greatly admired Babbage and his frequent tributes did much to draw attention to Babbage's work in the post-war years.

ANALYTICAL ENGINE MILL BY HENRY PREVOST BABBAGE, 1910

Babbage bequeathed his workshop, experimental work, drawings and other material relating to the Analytical Engine to his son Henry Prevost. To 'justify the confidence he had shown' in him, Henry wished to realise in metal some of his father's designs. This portion of the mill, the arithmetic unit and printing mechanism, was the result. It was worked on intermittently from the 1880s until 1910 in the workshop of W R Munro. It was designed to perform addition, subtraction, multiplication and division. Henry records that in 1910 it printed the first twenty two multiples of Pi to 28 places. These were later found to contain mistakes. It is questionable whether the machine ever worked reliably.

1896-58

"Who can foresee the consequences of such an invention?"
Ada Lovelace, 1843

"For the machine is not a thinking being, but simply an automaton which acts according to the laws imposed upon it."
Ada Lovelace, 1843

Polymath

The scope of Babbage's talents and interests is impressively wide even by the generous standards of Victorian polymathy. He was an inventor, reformer, mathematician, philosopher, scientist, outspoken critic of the scientific establishment, raconteur, traveller, political economist, socialite, one-time politician, incorrigible rationalist, anagrammatist, a visionary, and a prolific writer.

Babbage delighted in instruments and contrivances. Devices he designed and constructed include a 'black box' recorder for monitoring the condition of railway tracks, occulting lights for communication with ships, an ophthalmoscope (possibly the first), theatre lighting using coloured filters, a pen with rotatable discs for drawing broken lines on maps, a 'camper' (a four-wheel carriage used on one of his European tours, with sleeping accommodation, rudimentary cooking facilities and a commode), a device for delivering messages using aerial cables (a demonstration of his scheme for an intra-city funicular mail service), and footwear for walking on water (shoes with hinged flaps which spread on downward thrust).

BABBAGE'S SOCIAL DIARY OF 1844

Three months (April-June) in the diary indicate a full schedule of engagements including several meetings with the Duke of Somerset, a close friend, as well as portrait sittings with Samuel Laurence.

Dr N F Babbage, Australia

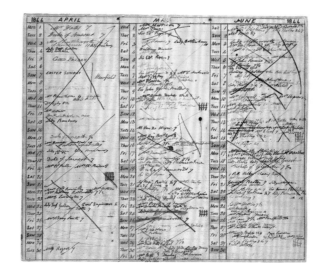

BABBAGE IN 1860

Photograph taken at the Fourth
International Statistical Congress in
London in 1860, when Babbage was an
alert 68; perhaps the last portrait in his
lifetime, this study was used for derivatives
including the half-tone frontispiece to
Babbage's calculating engines by his son
H P Babbage, published in 1889.

Mr B E C Howarth-Loomes

Devices he proposed or outlined include a tug boat for winching vessels upstream, diving bells, submarines propelled by compressed air, a games automaton for playing noughts and crosses, an altimeter, a seismograph, a flat-bottomed 'hydrofoil', a coronagraph for producing artificial eclipses, an emergency release coupling for railway carriages, speaking tubes linking London and Liverpool, and two forms of cow catcher.

Babbage foresaw the exhaustion of coal reserves and the use of tidal power. He maintained that if posterity was not ingenious enough to find an alternative to coal, mankind deserved to be frostbitten. He proposed a system of decimal currency and influenced the introduction of flat-rate postage. He advocated life peerages in preference to hereditary rank and was a vocal supporter of a free market economy.

LETTERS FROM THE DUKE OF SOMERSET

Babbage mixed with the social and intellectual élite of his day. He was a close friend and frequent dining companion of the Duke of Somerset. Eighteen invitations from the Duke are shown, importuning Babbage to visit and dine.

Dr S B Babbage, Australia

OCCULTING LIGHT: CLOCKWORK MECHANISM, c1899

Babbage devised a system of signalling using a light source that was alternately shuttered and revealed in a controlled sequence. He proposed such occulting lights for ship-to-ship and ship-to-shore communication. The sequence of occultations was controlled using a clockwork mechanism to operate the shutter. Babbage wrote that during the Great Exhibition of 1851 he displayed an occulting mechanism in the window of his house. He relates that people passing at night dropped calling cards into his letter box with the number being transmitted inscribed. The plaque with this device indicates that it was invented in 1850 by Babbage and that the apparatus was made by Henry Babbage in 1899.

The numerical sequence of the occultation is programmed by adjusting sliding circular plates (centre front) which determine how many of the teeth of the cam-plate are active for each portion of the sequence.

Totnes Museum

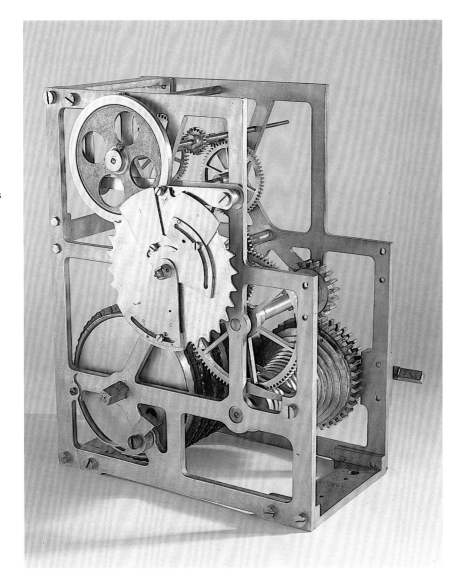

POSTER ANNOUNCING 'DEATH OF
MR. BABBAGE', 1871

Photograph by Oscar Rejlander; a
barefoot newsboy cries 'Second edition!'
with a poster for the *Pall Mall Gazette*, of
21 October 1871, a few days after
Babbage's death.

International Museum of Photography at
George Eastman House

Babbage had a significant influence as a reformer. He was prominent in the movement to revitalise mathematics in England by the introduction of Continental theories. His outspoken public attacks on the scientific establishment, particularly the Royal Society, drew attention to the neglect of science and the professional status of scientists.

He was highly sociable and a sought after guest in the best circles. Invitations to his own Saturday evening soirées were prized by members of the London social set. A contemporary wrote that 'one of three qualifications were necessary for those who sought to be invited – intellect, beauty and rank'. Wealth was, of itself, no recommendation.

His collected published works fill eleven volumes – six full length works and nearly ninety papers. Archives of unpublished material – letters, notebooks, and designs – contain material well in excess of this.

Babbage stood as a parliamentary candidate for the borough of Finsbury in 1832 and 1834 but lost on both occasions. He wrote a short play parodying his electioneering experiences. It closes with the central character, the well-meaning but politically ingenuous Turnstile, returning to his study after his unsuccessful campaign. He addresses his books and instruments as 'my old friends' whom he has neglected for the hustings. 'Tomorrow', says Turnstile, '[I] take leave of politics, and try to be myself once more'.

Babbage died on 18 October 1871. In a prophetic passage written towards the end of his life, he affirmed his conviction in the value of his work on calculating machines: 'If unwarned by my example, any man shall undertake and shall succeed in really constructing an engine . . . upon different principles or by simpler means, I have no fear of leaving my reputation in his charge, for he alone will be fully able to appreciate the nature of my efforts and the value of their results'.

SOCIÉTÉ FRANÇAISE
de Statistique Universelle.

LE ROI, PROTECTEUR.

DIPLOME DE MEMBRE HONORAIRE

DIPLOMAS AND AWARDS

Babbage was highly critical of the state of science in England and particularly the conduct of learned societies. This contrasts with his high regard for the scientific academies of France, Italy and Prussia. Babbage was honoured by many learned societies especially on the Continent where he was held in great esteem. The certificate shown is one of over thirty in a volume of his diplomas and awards.

Dr S B Babbage, Australia

Bibliography

IN MEMORIAM

The obituary record in *The Graphic*, 18 November 1871. The accompanying notice was largely appreciative of Charles Babbage's achievements.

The Graphic, vol. IV, no. 103, p.496

PRIMARY SOURCES

Published

Babbage studies have been hampered by the volume, diversity and physical dispersion of relevant material. Access to primary sources has been greatly increased by publication of *The works of Charles Babbage* ed. Martin Campbell-Kelly, London, Pickering, 1989. This eleven-volume set contains Babbage's complete known published writings as well as two hitherto unpublished items and fourteen items not written by Babbage. The material documents his deliberations on mathematical, philosophical, scientific, industrial, economic, social and political issues. It includes his 86 known papers and six full length works: *A comparative view of the various institutions for the assurance of lives* (1826), *Reflections on the decline of science in England, and on some of its causes* (1830), *On the economy of machinery and manufactures* (4th edition, 1835), *The ninth Bridgewater treatise* (2nd edition, 1838), *The Exposition of 1851; or views of the industry, the science, and the government, of England* (1851), and *Passages from the life of a philosopher* (1864). *Passages* is Babbage's anecdotal autobiography. It is a rewarding and entertaining read, rich in humour, self-parody and false modesty. A single-volume selection from the collected works is *Science and reform: selected works of Charles Babbage* ed. Anthony Hyman, Cambridge University Press, 1989.

A compendium of papers on the engines, collated and added to by Henry Prevost Babbage, was published in 1889 (London, Spon). This has been reprinted in facsimile in *Babbage's calculating engines*, Los Angeles, Tomash, 1989, with an introduction by Allan G Bromley. Selections from this and Babbage's *Passages from the life of a philosopher* are reprinted in *Charles Babbage and his calculating engines*, reissued as *Charles Babbage: on the principles and development of the calculator and other seminal writings* ed Philip Morrison and Emily Morrison, New York, Dover, 1961.

Memoirs of the life and labours of the late Charles Babbage, Esq. FRS ed. Anthony Hyman, Cambridge (Mass), London, MIT Press; Los Angeles, Tomash,

1988, is a biographical memoir written between 1872 and 1880 by H W Buxton, a colleague of Babbage. It contains material from manuscripts given by Babbage to Buxton and provides a sympathetic contemporary view of Babbage's work on his engines. All the above works have valuable introductory and editorial material.

Archival

Primary archival material is in the collections of the Science Museum Library (London), British Library Manuscripts Department (London), Cambridge University Library (Cambridge Philosophical Society Archives), Public Record Office (Kew Division, South West London; Chancery Lane Division, London), Museum of the History of Science (Oxford), Royal Society (London), and Wanganui Regional Museum (New Zealand).

Other registered archival material is in various libraries and museums. There is also material in several private collections and in the care of the Babbage family.

SECONDARY SOURCES

Irascible genius: a life of Charles Babbage, inventor by Maboth Moseley, London, Hutchinson, 1964. First biography of Babbage. Readable. Superseded by Hyman, 1982.

Charles Babbage, philosopher, reformer, inventor: a history of his contributions to science by Walter Lyle Bell. Doctoral dissertation, Oregon State University, 1975; Ann Arbor, University Microfilms.

Ada, Countess of Lovelace: Byron's legitimate daughter by Doris Langley Moore, London, John Murray, 1977. A thoroughgoing biography of Ada Lovelace.

The mathematical work of Charles Babbage by J M Dubbey, Cambridge University Press, 1978. Analysis and critique of Babbage's mathematical work.

Charles Babbage: pioneer of the computer by Anthony Hyman, Princeton University Press, 1982. Authoritative biography of Babbage. Particularly good on the context of the times.

Ada: a life and a legacy by Dorothy Stein, Cambridge (Mass), London, MIT Press, 1985. A controversial biography de-lionising Ada Lovelace.

Glory and failure: the difference engines of Johann Müller, Charles Babbage and Georg and Edvard Scheutz by Michael Lindgren. Trans. from Swedish by Craig G McKay, Linköping, 1987. Second ed., Cambridge (Mass), London, MIT Press, 1990. A detailed and lively treatment of the history and technology of the early difference engines. Originally a doctoral dissertation.

Computing before computers ed. William Aspray, Iowa State University Press, 1990. Chapter 2, 'Difference Engines and Analytical Engines' by Allan G Bromley is a concise and authoritative account of the design and operation of Babbage's engines.

The little engines that could've: the calculating machines of Charles Babbage by Bruce Collier. Doctoral dissertation, Harvard, 1970; New York, Garland, 1991.

PORTRAITS

A full iconography of Charles Babbage is lacking in the literature. The entry in the *Dictionary of national biography*, published in 1885, omits reference to his portraiture although several likenesses were known and exhibited in his lifetime and by 1881 an oil was documented in a public collection. Two portraits were exhibited in London in 1891-92, but

F Boase's *Modern English biography* (1892) cites two obituary engravings of 1871 in the popular press. (One of these is reproduced here on page 44.)

The British Museum's *Catalogue of engraved British portraits* by F O'Donoghue (1908) lists one print by John Linnell, (page 1) published by Colnaghi in 1833. The drawing of 1840 by William Brockedon (page 18), and the oil painting of 1845 by Samuel Laurence (page ii) in the National Portrait Gallery, London, are described in R Ormond's *Early Victorian portraits* (1973), together with a brief iconography; on display among the nineteenth century men of science is the daguerreotype of 1847-51 (page 24) by Antoine Claudet, acquired in 1977. These are noted in the Gallery's *Dictionary of British portraiture* (1979).

Other likenesses have come to light over the years. The location of at least two oil paintings and a miniature have still to be determined. Research so far indicates that some sixteen or more portraits in various media were executed over half a century during Babbage's life and posthumously. Almost every decade is represented, with an emphasis on the period through the 1840s when about eight portraits were completed, among them the most important, the Laurence oil which characterises Babbage as the eminent man of letters. Earlier studies, an engraving for the *Mechanics Magazine* of 1833 (page 6) and a drawing of c1836-37 by Laurence (page 30), move from conventional pose as an elegant man in society to pick up in their strength of facial expression the air of a man hounded by difficulties. The essence of portraiture of Babbage in advanced years is a mature but alert resignation, perceived more closely through the camera than with the artist's pencil.

Such a range is perhaps unusual for a Victorian mechanician and indicates something of the contemporary esteem for Babbage, whether including formal family portraits (page v) or probable commissions from notable artists of the day, or in advancing the new art of portraiture by experimental photography, for which much patience was required by the sitter. Additionally a number of portraits were studies taken at meetings of scientific associations. A photograph at a Statistical Congress in 1860, when Babbage was 68, seems to be the last portrait taken in his lifetime and became the basis for derivatives and posthumous works (page 39).

Among primary sources of evidence for portraits, Babbage's letters afford a tantalising glimpse of a wide social round of scientific discussions and engagements, including friendships with David Wilkie, William Mulready and other artists, invitations to exhibitions, and a mind of constant enquiry into new graphic art processes. *Wendy Sheridan*